AN UNCOMMON WAY TO WEALTH

AN UNCOMMON WAY TO WEALTH

BY
"VICTOR D'ARGENT"

Charterhouse Publishing
Dublin, Ireland

Published by exclusive arrangement for
The Ken Roberts Company, Inc.
by
Charterhouse Publishing Ltd.,
17 Windsor Place, Pembroke Street,
Dublin 2, Ireland.

Translation © 1994
by
The Ken Roberts Company, Inc.

ISBN 1 57098 009 8

EDITOR'S NOTE:

The author of this story uses the pseudonym "Victor D'Argent". He is believed to have become the head of one of the largest Parisian publishing houses, and to have assisted the careers of Gustave Flaubert, the celebrated author of *Madame Bovary*, and Victor Hugo, who became internationally famous for writing *Les Miserables*. D'Argent himself eventually became something of a recluse, widely sought for financial, artistic, and personal advice, but quite careful about revealing his secrets. Just a few days before his death, he delivered this story to a small, provincial publisher who printed only a few copies, unaware of the true identity of the author.

A badly damaged but complete copy of this original French edition of *An Uncommon Way to Wealth* was discovered amongst the private papers of a wealthy Anglo-Irish bachelor, who recently passed away. The copy was found in the late gentleman's home in County Cork by an antiquarian bookdealer from Dublin who had purchased the books remaining in the house from the heirs. The bookdealer made a gift of the book to the translator of this first English language edition.

WHEN I ENTERED THE RUE DE SAGESSE that morning, I had expected only the same motley collection of rabble rousers. Still, I said to myself, "Today will be your lucky day, Victor D'Argent. Today one of them will tell you what you need to know."

I had been strolling this street daily since late November, when I left the University, convinced that success in this new modern life could have no relation to the solemn, droning voices of my professors in their threadbare coats. "I might have been royalty, a Marquis!" I had shouted aloud as I stormed across the academy's grounds. This is the truth. Had it not been for the bourgeois revolution in 1789, which sent my grandfather to the guillotine and took from us all the riches of our royalty, I would have been one of the untouchable nobility, instead of a man living on odd jobs and the last remnants of the family fortune, a man without a future.

The Rue de Sagesse was full of all manner of contenders for my soul. Though I knew that they were neither wise nor honest, I could not resist the lure of their claims. The phrenologist stood his usual post behind a small chair at the top of the street, beckoning to me with the fervent promise that the future was hidden in the bumps on my head! This fellow had drawn the geography of my cranium more than once, and from him I had learned nothing more than the rather ordinary contours that encased my brain. And still he called after me, urgently, as if I were the only one left in the world who would listen to his nonsense. As I passed, six other fortune tellers came into view: lining the street to my right were the botomancer, cartomancer, crystallomancer, bibliomancer, rhabdomancer, and lithomancer[†], all shouting their appeals at once in a babble of

---

[†]EDITOR'S NOTE: Botomancy tells fortunes using the leaves of plants; cartomancy with Tarot or other playing cards; crystallomancy with a crystal ball; bibliomancy through interpreting the page at which a book (often the *Bible*) falls open; rhabdomancy through the use of a divining rod; and lithomancy with reference to the pattern made by tossed pebbles.

promises. I had studied each of their arts with great seriousness, filling my apartment with spellbooks, and an assortment of divining rods and crystal balls. But the consequence of this was, at bottom, no more than entertainment. And so I had re-directed my energies to the other side of the street, where stood the physiocrat, the healer, the confidence man, the royalist, and the elocutionist.

The physiocrat gave long speeches on the virtues of Quesnay's *Tableau Economique*, and urged all who gathered (on some days, a good number) to invest their lives and energies in agriculture. "Wealth is in the land," he would cry any number of times in his discourse, and his audience would repeat this incantation, until speaker and listeners eventually dissolved into a dull litany of empty sameness. I had once been one of his disciples, and had studied every word of Quesnay, and Adam Smith as well.[†] But no amount of economic

---

[†]EDITOR'S NOTE: Quesnay and Adam Smith are both well-known for advancing *laissez faire* theories of economics, which advocate the relaxation of constraints on the free market system.

theory opened a window into my own future and hoped-for fortunes.

The healer displayed shelves of elixirs: one for rheumatism, one for gout, and on and on. He had sold me a book once, promising that the chemical mixtures it contained would cleanse both the body and the mind. He insisted further that a healthy body and a clear head were the rudiments of worldly success, and that I would be a rich man in due course. Sad to say, most of the potions he prescribed made me sick, and the only person who became richer was the healer, as he pocketed my money with regularity.

The confidence man seemed sincere enough. He featured games of chance to passers-by, spinning a roulette wheel with his left hand and shaking dice with his right, while he advertised gambling as a sort of philosophy: "As we arise each day, we are once again the pawns of chance. Chance determines our failure, just as it governs our success. Give chance its due, and you may walk away a rich man." It seemed to many that he actually wanted them to win, though it almost never turned out that way. Seeing in me some unusual intelligence, or so I thought, the confidence man took me aside and offered to instruct me in his trade. It was then that I looked squarely into his eyes, saw only sadness, and quickly took my leave.

The royalist bemoaned the chaos that was France. "When we lost the nobility, we lost the only insurance that wealth would not fall to the rabble," he declared. "We must recapture the greatness of our nation, and deliver it from the evils of bourgeois democracy." I had occasion to reveal to him my noble roots, and his excitement was nearly intolerable. "You will have your good name again," he shouted with tremendous vigor each time I passed. Much as I thrilled at the prospect, I knew that he was wrong. I must admit that for a time I shared his hope, and as if to prepare myself for a rebirth of royalty, spent every spare moment reading the lives of French monarchs. But though I dreamed of leisure pomp, I still awoke each day in my dusty, common quarters.

The elocutionist was the grandest figure of them all. "Remember," he would say with perfectly dignified enunciation, "every word you speak must be precisely coordinated with the appropriate movements of head, arms, and torso."

As he said so, the man swept his arm across his body as if to demonstrate the dynamics of his oratory. "When your words and body operate in harmony," he continued, "all around you will approximate your perfection, and all strife will disappear." Hearing some sense in this, I had pored over stacks of diagrams that illustrated the accomplished orator issuing great dramatic performances, and had rehearsed hour upon hour the elements of eloquence. After some weeks of this, I had become merely a curiosity, responding to the simplest question from a neighbor with great movements of my head and legs, and large round tones of exaggerated pronunciation. The world around me did not settle into harmony; rather, its inhabitants began to flee my sight!

And so, here I was again on the Rue de Sagesse. But this time, a new contender for my soul stood around the bend at the end of the street. Let me explain: The Rue de Sagesse stretched some 1000 yards, and my habit was to walk its length from south to north. At the northern end, the street branched east and west. Turning east, one encountered the shops of local merchants, and might very well spend a pleasant enough time selecting some fruit and bread and wine for that day's meal. Most northerly travelers along the Rue de Sagesse did just this, and because the street was rather constantly full of tourists and locals alike, the merchants sitting at its end did quite well. I, however, had taken to turning west, away from the common traffic, to head into a corner of the adjoining woods, where I might be alone with my sober and often gloomy thoughts. There the newcomer stood, at the turn that few took but myself, looking strangely out of place for several reasons, not the least of which was her sex: she was a beautiful woman — slight, dark-haired, dressed in all white. She looked a seraph among debauchers on this row of clamorous men. I had not seen her before, yet she seemed to know something of me, for here she was waiting, as if for my arrival.

A large hawthorne grew in that spot, but it was not yet late enough in the season for it to bear fruit. The seraph threw handfuls of small dark particles — they appeared to be tiny seeds — in the direction of the tree, and much to my astonishment and consternation, she threw some of these seeds directly at me, as if I were myself a thorn tree. She looked at me directly. Her expression was blank, and when she spoke, the voice seemed to be coming through her, from some other source. The words were, I supposed then, no more than mad ramblings:

> *Life is more than food, and the body*
> *more than clothing. Be dressed for*
> *action and have your lamps lit.*
> *Blessed are those slaves whom the*
> *master finds alert when he comes.*
>
> *This is the unexpected hour. Are*
> *you at work? The master is arriving!*
> *Strive to enter through the narrow*
> *door. Find the coin that is lost.*

With that, she tossed more seeds upon me.

"Why do you say these things?" Without answering, the seraph reached into a small pouch she wore at her waist, removed a gold coin, and flung it just behind the thorn tree, out of my sight. Feeling a bit foolish, but determined to learn the nature of this strange figure, I strode to the spot where the coin had landed, and with some effort combed the low-lying foliage and located the object. When I turned back, the seraph was gone.

I stared down at the coin. It bore the marks of no official currency. Instead, there was on one side the imprint of some form of vegetation that I could not identify, with slender branches and leaves and what appeared to be tiny flowers. On the reverse was the imprint of an open door. What could these symbols mean? Somehow they were connected to the seraph's final words: "Strive to enter through the narrow door. Find the coin that is lost." Perhaps, I thought, there is a treasure to be found, lost coins hidden behind a narrow door! Yes, perhaps here at last was the answer to my needs, a mysterious messenger who would lead me to gold!

I determined to ask the Confidence Man what to make of the coin, in a casual sort of way, taking care not to reveal so much about my meeting with the seraph that his own greed was awakened. I hurried back up the Rue de Sagesse, clutching the coin in my wet palm.

"Look at what I found in the gutter," I said, feigning amusement as I displayed the coin to my gambling friend. He looked at both sides, and whispered with a sigh, "St. Germaine." Thinking this utterance to be some kind of curse, I asked what was wrong.

"You would do well to ignore this coin," he said. "Those who try to find its owner are fools. I can attest personally to that."

"Tell me what you mean, I beg of you." I tugged urgently at his arm as he turned away.

"Well," he paused. "You probably should know, lest you do something foolish. It is believed that St. Germaine lives in a castle on the dark side of the Hartz mountains†, and that the castle is surrounded by large black mustard plants, each twelve feet tall, a most unusual sight. Such is the plant pictured on this coin. When St. Germaine was born, no one knows. It is said that he has been alive, amassing wealth, for over two thousand years. He creates these coins himself, making gold from common lead, in the fashion of a genuine alchemist. I myself made the journey to Hanover, determined to pledge myself to St. Germaine and learn his secrets. I combed the Hartz Mountains, day after day, but never located

†EDITOR'S NOTE: The Hartz Mountains are located in Hanover, several hundred miles northeast of Paris. In the eighteenth and nineteenth centuries, they were often associated with magical phenomena.

any castle, only a few huts populated by peasants. This St. Germaine does not exist! A coin shows up now and then, but I am convinced that their appearance is someone's idea of a joke."

I trudged home, confused and forlorn. Should I believe the Confidence Man? After all, deception was his stock in trade. Perhaps he knew more, or other, than he was telling. The seraph's appearance certainly did not seem to be a joke. And her words. I had encountered them somewhere before. They had a familiar ring. Reaching my small cell, I sat down at my desk, still deep in dark thought. My hand fell upon the *Bible* that lay at the edge of the desk, and feeling both whimsical and anxious, I decided to try some of the bibliomancer's art. Sitting the book on its edge, I allowed it to fall open. The page was from Matthew, Chapter 13. I began to read a passage that, for some reason I could not remember, I had marked when I read it some months, or years ago:

> *The kingdom of heaven is like to a*
> *grain of a mustard seed, which a man*
> *took, and sowed in his field: Which*
> *indeed is the least of all seeds: but*

*when it is grown, it is the greatest
among herbs, and becometh a tree, so
that the birds of the air come and
lodge in the branches thereof.*

I picked one of the seeds that the seraph had thrown from my hair and stared at it. Yes, it was a mustard seed! And the Confidence Man had said that the tree on the coin was a mustard plant!

What could this all mean? I was ready to dismiss all of it as sheer coincidence, but quite a strange and irresistible feeling was overtaking me. I can describe it only as . . . inspiration! I began packing, determined to go to Hanover and find St. Germaine. I scarcely remember now the particulars of my trip, only that within some few days I found myself at the foot of the Hartz mountains, clutching the seraph's coin in my hand. I began to walk, uncertain of my destination, but filled with a determination to continue until I either sank exhausted or located St. Germaine's castle. "Perhaps this *is* the way to the kingdom of heaven," I thought with a little smile. "Walking myself to death in this strange and treacherous territory." But suicide was not my aim. Yet, I was aimless.

Aimless and inspired! The stuff of insanity, I told myself. What could that castle hold for me? Gold? This was all I could imagine as my reward, yet it was not lust for gold that was driving me.

I walked for hours, and as the sun began to set, I resigned myself to facing cold darkness, and perhaps death. Then, in the twilight, I saw it. Just a few yards ahead, too close to have gone unnoticed until this moment. A large, grand structure that reminded me of the Chateau de Chambord that I so admired.[†] Then darkness fell, and I could see nothing. Thinking my vision a mirage, I sank.

When I awoke it was dawn. I was not frozen to death. In fact, I was comfortably warm, and felt well-rested. And my vision had not been a mirage. It was as if the Chateau de Chambord had been transported to this spot. I could see that it was all there: the perfectly symmetrical square flanked by four round towers, with gleaming windows placed precisely above one another on all

[†] EDITOR'S NOTE: The Chateau de Chambord was built by King Francis I of France (1515-47), and is an exemplary model of the post-medieval French *chateau de plaisance* that was used as a country house for royalty.

three levels, all surrounded by a moat. The bridge was down, as if to welcome me, and as I walked toward the chateau I noticed that it was surrounded by large trees that resembled — yes — the picture on the seraph's coin! Once across the bridge, I stood before a most unusual door, too narrow by far for any adult to pass through easily.

Then I saw her, the seraph, standing just beyond the opening. She was beckoning to me, and calling: "The master is arriving! Strive to enter through the narrow door!" With ferocious exertion, I pushed myself through the opening.

She had waited for me, and led me along a narrow corridor to a spiral staircase. I followed her up, and saw that the staircase opened into a suite of apartments. Then she left me, suddenly, and I felt lost again. The sound of laughter aroused me, and I followed it into one of the apartments, where I found a man sitting on a large chair facing the window that looked out on the very spot where I had collapsed the night before.

"Come in, D'Argent." His voice was strong, and he was smiling. He was dressed exquisitely, in bright silks, and as he stood I could see that we were both about the same height. He looked not much older than I, and as I recalled that St. Germaine was believed to have lived for hundreds of years, I supposed that this fellow was some assistant. "Look about. See where you are," he said. I surveyed the room. There was one wall filled with books, whose titles — all in languages other than French — I could not understand. A harpsichord stood against another wall, with a violin atop it. And in a corner of the room sat a small chest, filled so high that its lid would not close, and I could see that the contents gleamed like — gold.

"Where are you?" he asked.

I was taken aback, and answered slowly, "In the palace of the Count of St. Germaine?"

"You are not answering my question. I shall ask it again. Where are you?"

I tried again: "In the Hartz Mountains, in Hanover?"

"This is not a party game," he said, smiling. "I can do you no good if you cannot answer a simple question. Once more, where are you?"

"I am not sure," I confessed.

"Very well, now we can begin," the man said.

"Please sit down."

Two servants in crisp uniforms entered, each carrying a bright gold tray. One was piled with fruit and bread, the other held crystal goblets and bottles of wine. As they set the trays down between the man and I, he asked me another question.

"What do you wish?"

My mind began to race. What should I say? Gold? Yes, surely he would understand. A man in such opulent surroundings, living in such luxury, would surely understand the desires of a disenfranchised nobleman. Perhaps he had heard of my plight, I thought. Perhaps he used his own wealth to restore the birthright of others. Or perhaps . . .

"What do you wish?"

"The wealth that is my birthright. Gold."

He laughed. "You have given me two answers. And you must not suppose that they are the same thing. Possessing gold is an easy matter, for anyone with a measure of patience, discipline, and intelligence. But the wealth that is your birthright, that is something else again. It will take me some time to teach you how to attain such wealth. Perhaps we should address your wish for gold first, so to dispense with the trivial and make way for matters of importance.

"Go to that chest in the corner, and bring back ten coins. Place them here on the table before us." I did so eagerly, and saw that, just as I had suspected, the chest was filled nearly to overflowing with gold.

The man stared for a moment at the coins I had spread before him, laughed, and then began his instruction: "Most men know nothing about how gold is created, and how its quantity grows. I am not speaking here of alchemy, you understand. It is quite true that I can, through alchemical means, create all the gold I wish. However, I have chosen to materialize only what you see in that chest, for the purposes of illustrating financial principles to worthy young men. All of my additional monies, a huge aggregate, I have earned through precisely the activities that I will now describe to you.

"Understand, first of all, that the financial world operates with reference to three primary markets: stocks, bonds, and gold. The first joint-stock companies were formed in England some two hundred years ago, and I was pleased to be the advisor of the founding merchants."

I was amazed at this revelation, but remained silent, fearing that any interruption might prevent the Count (surely it must be him) from continuing his instruction.

"Since then," he said, smiling at what must have been a telling expression on my face, "I have watched closely the behavior of all three markets and have noted what has become an economic fact: One of the three major markets is *always* rising. Therefore, anyone who holds investments in all three will be profiting in at least one of them at any given moment. But very few people understand this — they confuse diversifying an investment with diluting it, and think that remaining in one market only is safer. The truth is that when the value of one of these three markets is falling, the value of one or both of the others will be rising. Therefore, your loss in one is compensated by a gain in another. And, as we shall see shortly, a falling market offers you the opportunity to buy more for less!"

The Count seemed to sense that I was becoming overwhelmed, and he paused for a moment before continuing.

"We will focus on these pieces of gold, but you must know that the principles of investment I will disclose are universal, and work impressively in any market. They will also guide you in deciding which market will assure you the greatest profit at any time.

"You must realize that the world has entered a new era, in which noble blood is no guard against economic failure, and no insurance of economic success. If you seek monetary wealth, you must use economic laws to your advantage, and no matter what your station in life, you will prosper.

"Most men never initiate any effective investment plan, because they do not understand precisely how money grows. Here is a simple formula for predicting how your money can double at regular intervals: Let us say that you deposit these ten coins in an account at that small bank along the eastern branch of the Rue de Sagesse, and are promised interest on your investment at the annual rate of ten percent. I can assure you that in just over seven years you will have twenty gold pieces, and if you wait that long yet again you will have forty. That is, your money will increase four-fold in just about fourteen and one-half years, with no exertion at all on your part!"

"How is this done?" I wondered aloud.

"Money multiplies at a predictable rate, whenever the rate of interest remains constant. Simply take the interest rate you are earning, and divide it into what many of my students have called the "magic number": 72. So you see that an interest rate of 10 percent, divided into 72, yields 7.2. This is the number of years required for your money to double. And given an additional 7.2 years, it will double again! You see that there is no mystery to determining how long it will take to achieve a financial goal, if you know this magic number.

"Just as it is possible to predict how the money you invest will behave, it is also possible to predict how the money you save will behave, presuming you do save money on a regular basis." At this point the Count laughed again. He seemed to know that the idea of investing or saving money was alien to me. Because I considered myself a nobleman, above all "bourgeois" methods of accumulating money, I had remained ignorant of principles that were — I was beginning to believe — immensely valuable.

The Count continued: "I will impress the value of saving upon you shortly. For now, let us presume that you are wise enough to save a part of your earnings. Let us say that you save ten coins each year, depositing them in the bank, at an interest rate of ten percent. How much gold will you have deposited in — let us say — fourteen years?"

"Why, 140 pieces," I answered, already feeling wealthy at the very thought of owning 140 pieces of gold.

"Yes, but as the great Willsford[†] said in 1640 (at my urging), the *compound* interest that you earn on such a deposit is 'interest upon interest'. With this in mind, you can calculate the point at which you will have twice as much gold as you have deposited. And in this case, it is the magic number 144 which tells you when the process of compound interest will lead your money to double. Simply divide the rate of interest, 10, into 144. The quotient is 14.4. Thus, the period required to double your annual investment of 10 pieces of gold is 14.4 years. At that time, you will have deposited 140 pieces, but you will own 280 pieces!"

[†]EDITOR'S NOTE: T. Willsford was the author of *Scales of Commerce* in 1640.

"This is marvelous," I said. "But surely such transformations must involve actual magic of some sort."

The Count laughed. "Not at all. This is simple and irrefutable arithmetic. If you deposit your gold at a constant rate of interest, it *must* grow, and at predictable points it will double, and double again, and again."

"I see that amassing a small fortune could be quite simple, given patience and some capital," I said.

"Yes, this is true. However, most men, when they earn a bit of money, go out immediately and spend it on petty luxuries, and quickly become penniless again. The wise few set aside one-tenth of all that they earn. That is, they *pay themselves first*, before they pay others. If you do this with consistency, you will activate natural principles — such as the magic numbers 72 and 144 — that will dramatically increase your capital. You see, saving money is not an act of frugality, as many believe. Rather, it is a demonstration of your sincere respect for your capital. In other words, placing money aside for yourself is a psychological and spiritual virtue. Some these days accuse those who save their money regularly, and who nurture its growth, of being 'capitalists' who over-value material goods. I say that only if you act with wisdom and respect toward the material wealth you earn, will you ever develop the personal discipline required for your full growth as a human being."

I did not fully understand this, and the Count seemed to sense my confusion. He patted me on the shoulder, as if to say, "Don't worry, understanding will come," and then continued.

"However, you must take care not to hoard your gold. Realize that money behaves like a natural force. I do not mean by this merely that gold is a naturally occurring precious metal nourished by the earth, although this is quite true. But most men do not realize that *money multiplies through distribution.*

"All of life, including the life of any piece of currency, is dependent upon the dynamics of exchange and reciprocation. Think of yourself entering a crowded room. You say a word to one person or another as you pass, you hear a conversation that seems to interest you, and you join in. At some point you make a witty remark about, shall we say, the cost of wine in Paris. All the time, people drift in and out of this conversation, and circulate about the room. You do this as well. Some hours later, to your surprise, you hear someone talking about an exceptionally fine wine that comes from a little-known vineyard on the outskirts of Paris. He says, 'Given the cost of wine in Paris, one need only travel a few miles to find a splendid and well-priced product.' You realize that somehow, your earlier comment had migrated into this scene, and activated this valuable little bit of information, which has now returned to you.

"When you send money out into what I might call the 'financial conversation', it behaves likewise, moving in ways that are not wholly predictable, but always returning to you in some enhanced form. The source of your 'windfall' will be a surprise, but if you were able to trace its origins, you would locate that original moment — perhaps an act of generosity or kindness, perhaps the payment of a debt, perhaps an investment into a business enterprise — when you sent your money off on its 'journey'."

"Is my encounter with you to be understood as some sort of 'windfall', as the result of some earlier act of mine?" I asked.

"Of course," the Count laughed. "You will understand all of this in time. At the moment, I must stress that, although we have been speaking of the interest or return on your investment as a steady, consistent rate, the financial market rarely behaves in this way. The interest rate that a bank pays will fluctuate according to the conditions of the three major markets. Just so, the value of any product that is traded on the open market varies constantly. In the winter, the price of wood is higher than it is in the summer, is it not? This is because our need for warmth has increased, and the value of wood for heating follows.

"Now, few men invest in what I shall call 'commodities'. By commodity, I mean simply, any article that can be bought or sold, from ounces of gold or silver, to fields of wheat. As the great philosopher John Locke said to me when he was writing his fine essay on 'Money' in 1691, 'Commodities are Moveables, valuable by Money.' The worth of any commodity is changeable, and skill in predicting such changes can make a man rich. For instance, if I buy up wagonloads of wood in July, when prices are low, in anticipation of its increased demand in December, I am sure to profit. However, this skill for anticipating the future of a commodity is one that will not be fully realized — I expect — until well into the next century, when financial markets and the strategies for profiting in them will have arrived at a stage of tremendous sophistication.

"Even so, there are effective ways of profiting from the changing worth of a commodity even now, when our economics is still in a rather primitive state." The Count laughed again as he said this. "You are aware, I would hope, that the worth of precious metals such as gold and silver fluctuates constantly."

I nodded, even though it was true that I had not the slightest knowledge of the economics of gold and silver.

"Let us say that you receive a wage of one hundred francs each month, and you would like to devote twenty francs to purchasing shares of gold, measured in grams. You hope that the value of your gold will rise, and that you will be able to sell part of it occasionally at a tidy profit. But here is the eternal problem: *When do you sell?* How would you know if — had you waited a bit longer — the worth of your gold might have risen even higher? On the other hand, what if you wait too long, and the worth of your gold drops precipitously? You see, the perfect timing of buying and selling requires powers of prognostication that few possess." At this the Count smiled, and said in a tone of warning, "Many will cross your path who claim to know the future, and they will ask that you place your affairs in the charge of their 'special powers'. When this occurs, remember that although the predictions that *I* deliver will indeed come true, there are few others on earth like me.

"So let us make it simple for you to profit," he continued. I listened intently.

"I will continue, as I have, to give my illustrations with simple numbers, and with reference to familiar units of measure and currencies. However, you should realize that the principles I am revealing work for all values, in all societies and comparable economic systems.

"You wish, we shall presume, to add twenty francs worth of gold to your account each month. You begin to purchase gold on January 1, when one gram is valued at thirty francs. You buy two-thirds of one gram, and are at that moment the owner of twenty francs worth of gold.

"On February 1, you want your account to be worth forty francs. You inquire about the price of gold, and find that the value of gold has risen, so that one gram is valued at forty francs. You already have in your possession two-thirds of one gram, which is now worth two-thirds of forty francs, that is, more than twenty-six francs! By spending only fourteen francs, you will purchase enough gold to bring its total worth to forty francs. Your 'profit' for this month is the twenty francs you had been prepared to spend, minus the fourteen francs you actually spent. In other words, your profit is six francs."

I was beginning to understand. And even though the amount of profit he calculated was by no means munificent, it was exciting to know the mechanisms by which I could capitalize in an automatical manner on my investment. Without such knowledge, I surmised, buying and selling on the open market would be futile guesswork.

"Let us continue this process for a month or two," the Count said. "It is March 1. You inquire about the price of gold, and find that it has risen yet again, so that one gram is valued at forty-five francs. You bought two-thirds of one gram on January 1, and on February 1 you spent fourteen francs to buy fourteen-fortieths, or seven-twentieths, of one gram. Perhaps at this point we should do our calculations using the decimal system. I tried it awhile ago, when I was teaching you compound interest, but I was not entirely sure that my calculations were clear to you."

I bridled a bit at his implication that my powers of arithmetic were weak. "I can calculate mentally quite well," I said decisively, "and my familiarity with the decimal system is quite good." What I did not admit was that I had spent months and months of sleepless nights imagining my acquisition of great wealth, and had sharpened my powers of arithmetic through countless imaginary calculations.

"There, there, I mean no offense," the Count assured me. "It is just that so many young men intent upon gaining more money have never mastered simple arithmetic. I would expect that anyone of your age and breeding should know the decimal system, but I constantly find that ever since I helped introduce the system into Europe over five hundred years ago [here he paused, as if for effect], it is still learned thoroughly by so few.

"To continue then," the Count said, drawing out a piece of parchment from a drawer in the table before us, and wetting a fine silver pen with ink, "we will write out the values to two decimal places:

January — .67 grams
February — .35 grams

"You can see that on March 1, you are in possession of 1.02 grams of gold. Because gold is worth forty-five francs per gram on this date, the quantity you already possess is worth forty-five multiplied by 1.02, or 45.9 francs." He wrote out this calculation.

"Recall that you wish to increase the worth of your gold by twenty francs each month, so that on this date, March 1, you would like to buy enough gold to increase its worth to 60 francs. The difference between 60 and 45.9 is 14.1. So, you must spend slightly more than fourteen francs to have acquired the total you desire. Once again, since you were prepared to spend twenty francs, and were required to only spend just over fourteen, you have realized another profit, of nearly six francs."

I was beginning to imagine months of profit, and seeming to sense this, the Count raised his voice slightly to recapture my attention.

"Lest you imagine that each month will bring new profits, let me stress that the prices of precious metals — as with virtually any goods — can fluctuate in either direction. Recall that on March 1 you spent 14.1 francs, and the price of one gram of gold then was forty-five francs. Therefore, your 14.1 francs bought you .31 grams of gold. Your total, then, runs as follows:

January — *.67 grams*
February — *.35 grams*
March — *.31 grams*

"As you stand ready to buy again on April 1, you own 1.33 grams. However, the price of gold is now lower — only thirty-two francs per gram — so that your total worth is thirty-two multiplied by 1.33, or 42.56 francs. And now, on April 1, your goal is the ownership of eighty francs worth of gold! Clearly, this month you must spend *more* than your allotted twenty francs to reach your goal. You must buy 37.44 francs worth of gold. If you have held onto your profits from February and March, using them now will soften your loss somewhat, and in addition, you should realize that because the price of gold is low, your francs will buy a sizable quantity which will appreciate when the price of gold rises again. And let me assure you, it *will* rise.

"If you continue the process I have described here over time, and proceed with discipline and patience, you are likely to realize a net profit, and you are less likely to be buffetted violently by the vicissitudes of the market."

"What shall I call this marvelous process," I inquired?

"Since your profit results from the average value of your purchases over time, you might call this process 'value averaging'. I expect that this is what it will be called when it becomes more fully propagated in the future. However, I doubt that many will take advantage of it. Too many men are too impatient to be wise.

"Ah, the sun is high. We must rest," the Count said suddenly, rising to his feet. I, however, was anxious to continue: "But I am not the least bit fatigued," I insisted. "And I cannot imagine resting until you have revealed to me more of these secrets. And even then, I am afraid that my mind will be so full, that there will be no space for rest."

"If you truly want to learn and understand all I am saying," the Count said, resting his hand on my shoulder and smiling, you must stop thinking about it."

I must have looked incredibly surprised and confused, for the Count continued, "Your alarm is understandable. Surely this must strike you as a most unusual idea. But be aware that if you would lead a truly exceptional life, you must see the truth and wisdom in ideas which the great mass of men dismiss out of hand.

"You must understand, in this case, how the human mind works. When we are at rest, and the mind is not actively taking in information, it sorts through what it has heard, and stores it permanently. The Imagination also participates in this sorting and storing process, connecting the new information just heard with older information, and creating new associations and original ideas. It is because of this mental process that we always have a new idea, or conceive the solution of a problem, at an odd moment when we have actually stopped rehearsing it! This process governs those abrupt awakenings in the middle of the night, when we suddenly utter that same phrase attributed to Archimedes, 'Eureka!' In other words, clarity comes in a momentary flash when we least expect it, and can be encouraged only by a digression from the problem at hand, into rest or recreation."[†]

With this, he led me out of the room and down a long hallway into a bedroom that was beautifully appointed, with a bed that looked so soft and warm that resting upon it seemed especially inviting. "I shall be in the adjoining room," he said, and with that he left.

Although I did not disbelieve what the Count had said, I could not rest. I found a deck of playing cards in the drawer of the bedstand, and occu-

---

[†] EDITOR'S NOTE: The Count is here relating a process that twentieth century psychologists have verified. Creativity, they conclude, only occurs following some period of "incubation", as the mind synthesizes information apart from any deliberate effort by the "thinker".

pied myself with a game of Patience.[†] After some time — I could not tell how much time had passed, there being no clocks in this room or in the castle I had yet seen — a striking mental image appeared to me: a list of figures for the remainder of the "year" that the Count had begun in his instruction on value averaging. It seems that my mind had — without my knowledge — conceived a speculative history of fluctuations in the prices of gold, and had worked through all the arithmetic connected with profits and losses. Quickly I searched for paper and pen and wrote out all that I saw in my mind's eye. The process that had seemed rather difficult while the Count was explaining it, now struck me as remarkably clear and sensible.

Anxious to share my excitement, I opened the door to the adjoining room, and met a startling sight. The Count lay upon the top of the bed in perfect stillness, with a fixed gaze, apparently in deep meditation. He took no notice of my presence, because — I supposed — he was turned so completely inward. I recalled reading that this posture was common to both philosophers and orators in Greek and Roman antiquity; they trained themselves to achieve a state of deep medi-

[†]EDITOR'S NOTE: Patience was another name for Solitaire.

tation as they conceived their greatest discourses and public speeches.[†]

I left him to his thoughts, which were no doubt profound, and returned to my room to wait.

In time, there was a soft knock on my door, and the Count entered. "We shall continue," he announced, and led me back to the scene of our original meeting. I saw that the table had been replenished with refreshments, and feeling quite hungry, set immediately to eating.

The Count laughed. "Are you usually prone to eat whatever is put before you?" he asked. Startled, I realized that I was consuming food-stuffs with great abandon, and was a bit embarassed.

"Fortunately," the Count continued, "I have served you the purest and most healthful of food and drink, and the same is true of the information upon which you are 'feeding' today. But one should never be so quickly confident that the suppliers of one's body and mind are thus trustworthy. You must inspect and select carefully all that

[†] EDITOR'S NOTE: See, for instance, Cicero's *De Oratore* 3.5.

you eat and drink. If you take in pure foods and pure waters, your body will more easily maintain the purity and strength of its flesh, bone, muscle, and intellect.

"Regarding our financial discussions, let me caution you to be as careful about the suppliers of advice regarding money as you are about those who feed your body. Give thought to all of the advice that you receive, but respect only that advice that comes from experienced experts. Make certain that those who promise you profit are the beneficiaries of their own advice. One would not learn how to raise and nurture a child from one who is childless!

"Now, what do you do?" he asked.

"Do?" I repeated, feeling somewhat like a parrot. "I am not sure what you mean."

"Yes, I am not surprised," he laughed. "Few can answer this question. For one who sees himself as royalty, as someone who should live on the sweat of others simply by virtue of a name, it is especially difficult to realize that you must *do* something with your life. Where, for instance, do you expect to get the money for the different kinds of investments we have been reviewing?"

"Well," I said slowly. "I had hoped that you might become my benefactor."

"Ha!" shouted the Count, and this time there was no merriment in it. "Let me assure you of something, Victor D'Argent. You will leave this castle with no more than you owned when you arrived. Your entire cache of gold will consist of the one piece you have in your purse at present. And you will never see me again. However, what you will hear before your departure, indeed what you have heard to this moment, will have the potential to make you one of the wealthiest men in the world.

"Now, as to the matter of what you do," the Count continued, seating himself before the table once again. "You are at present what I would call a seeker, and this is not altogether bad. You have wandered the Rue de Sagesse, seeking different kinds of wisdom, working at this job or that, trying out this or that philosophy. You have, in this pursuit, been continually frustrated, have you not?"

"Yes, this is true," I answered with deep regret.

"But you must realize, and indeed you have

begun to realize, that your frustration was inevitable. For you see, all of the enterprises and philosophies operating along the Rue de Sagesse were simply illustrations of the common beliefs that one finds far and wide, beliefs that go in and out of fashion. In other words, there is no real wisdom along this 'Street of Wisdom'. You seem finally to have realized this, by choosing the path leading away from the crowds. You seem finally to have realized that your place in this life is not with them. This is why I called you here. But soon you must decide what to do."

"You mean that I must find work?" I asked.

"Well, it is true that you cannot partake of the financial conversation if you are not somehow generating finance. The last of your family fortune will soon run out. Further, although working at odd jobs will broaden your experience, it will keep you the servant of others, rather than your own master. At the same time, it is true that you must probably spend some time as an employee before you have the foundations for creating an enterprise of your own. What do you like to do?"

At first afraid that this was another impossible question, I realized that there was one activity that had remained constant, nearly obsessive, since I began my career as what the Count had called a seeker. "I like to read," I answered, visualizing the groaning bookshelves in my apartment, filled with every sort of manual for personal success, from the *Bible* to the *Bibliomancer's Handbook*.[†]

"Yes, you do," said the Count, with a tone of great approval. And for a seeker who is also a reader it would seem that the business of publishing is ideal?"

"Publishing?" I responded, having little idea to what sort of enterprise this term could refer.

"Yes. Few realize that we are at the beginning of what will be a golden age of publishing. It is at present a field that is uncrowded, ideal for the investment of your time and resources. There are indeed a small number of great publishing houses, in Paris and London, in Leiden and Antwerp, and even in America. However, when I say that the field is uncrowded, I mean that there is room for the publication of more and more books. The mar-

[†]EDITOR'S NOTE: This title does not appear in any bibliographies of nineteenth century European books in print, so it is possible that either D'Argent is mistaken, or that the book he names was never officially recorded.

ket has scarcely been tapped.

"It is only recently that writing has begun to provide a good living for authors, and this is largely because the general public has become a reading public. Evangelical Christians continue to distribute Bibles everywhere, and to teach others how to read them, and in so doing they are increasing the overall level of literacy, and ensuring the growing demand for books of all sorts.

"Once the new, mechanized printing press was put into use in 1811 (invented by my friend Frederick Koenig, I might add), it became possible to produce one thousand printed pages in an hour. And I predict with some certainty that one hundred years hence the presses will be printing more than one million pages in an hour, with no end of the voracious demand by the public for more reading!"

"Your knowledge of the publishing industry is impressive," I remarked.

The Count laughed. "I am simply addressing the issues that anyone — especially a young man in search of a career — must consider before investing his time and wage-earning skills in a business. Indeed, these are the issues you must consider before you devote yourself or your money to any enterprise. Permit me to summarize. You must find out first, whether a demand for the products of this enterprise will continue for years to come. To determine this, you must study its history. In this case, I have reviewed some of the history of printing and publishing, but should you decide to seek employment at a particular house (for instance, the new but burgeoning business of John Wiley in America), you must ascertain its specific history and learn about its executive personnel. Further, you must be assured that the house you would join — or looking ahead, the house you would buy — is alert to new markets. For instance, with the recent invention of photography by my friend Louis Daguerre, we now have the possibility of new kinds of pictorial representation in books. A publishing house that is not alert to this possibility and the demand it is sure to create is one in which you should not waste your time. Finally, if you are assured that the business in question is farsighted (not foolishly so, however), you must be sure you are not joining a business whose value has fluctuated dramatically since its inception, or whose debts are unreasonable."

"You are presuming," I ventured, "that such a business would hire such a one as me."

"That is true," the Count said, nodding. "However, let me assure you that any executive who does not appreciate your active interest in the state of his company, and want to reward that interest with a job, is probably not one from which you will learn much, or one whose business will remain successful for very long. The man who rejects your interest and intelligence is one who isolates himself from new ideas and progress, and he will eventually fail. You will learn most from one who is a true leader, and you must look for qualities of leadership not only in your employer, but in all whom you would place your trust, from the banker who manages your money to the physician who helps to manage your health."

"What is a leader, then?" I asked, feeling a bit foolish at voicing what seemed a quite elementary question. But I sensed that this was a question that few apart from the Count could answer correctly.

"An excellent question," the Count laughed. A leader will never require what he does not already exemplify. He will be a model of those virtues that increase wealth, namely, patience and thrift, and will have no personal habits that are destructive to the body, mind, spirit, or business. He will listen much more than he speaks, and rarely interrupt. This especially is an act of great difficulty, for most want to constantly profess their ignorance, rather than be silent and learn.

"A leader will treat his workers well, maintaining a relationship with them that is balanced between familiarity and strictness. He will never speak a harsh word to a worker except in private, where his criticisms will be fair and precise. Faced with a sudden challenge or problem, he remains calm and his mind remains open to new ideas."

The Count fell silent for a few moments. Eager to get us back to a discussion of my career, I asked, "What sort of publishing job should I look for?"

"None," the Count answered, and fell silent again.

Somehow, I felt compelled into silence myself, and at the same time, overwhelmed by terror. It suddenly became quite clear to me that I could no longer spend my life as a dilettante, that I must focus my energies on the sorts of success the Count had outlined. But at the same time, I realized that the way into future prosperity and happiness was uncertain. When one becomes part of the "financial conversation", one is subjected to what the Count had called the "dynamics of exchange and reciprocation". I felt as if I must enter the "crowded room" of competitive markets and ideas that the Count had described, but that for me, the room would be dark — terrifyingly dark. Urgent to shed some light on my future, I asked again, "What sort of publishing job should I look for?"

This time the Count laughed his characteristic laugh. "None, I tell you. The last thing you want is to be imprisoned in a job!"

"But I am not royalty, or rich like you. We both know that!" I felt myself redden with irritation.

"Now, now, please try to put aside the fear that is feeding your anger, and listen," he said softly. I tried to compose myself.

"The terror and confusion you are feeling are signs that you are headed, shall we say, in the right direction. Those who never experience these feelings are those who spend their lives following someone else's directions, rather than striking out on their own."

"But am I not preparing to follow your directions?" I asked.

"Not at all," he said, waving his hand in the air as if to dismiss my question altogether. "I cannot give you *directions*. I can only tell you the truth. Then you must direct yourself."

"But why do you tell me to have no job?" I persisted.

"Of your present acquaintances, who holds the most secure job?" he asked.

"Why, Jacques, I suppose. He has been a clerk at the local mill for some years now, and he is such a familiar figure and such a dutiful worker that no one could imagine his dismissal."

"I suppose, then, that Jacques is thoroughly acquainted with all aspects of the mill's operation."

"No," I answered after a moment's thought. "In fact, Jacques knows nothing except the papers that cross his desk. He has told me that the activities of the 'labor', as he calls them, are none of his affair."

"Well then, I suppose that Jacques dreams of

some day managing the mill himself. Surely he aspires to some greater position than that of a clerk."

"I don't think so. He said to me just recently, 'As long as I do my job and know my place, there will be food on the table for my wife and children.'"

"Alas," the Count sighed, for the first time since I had arrived. "This is the result of having a job. One lives with such fear of losing it, that the thought of venturing outside its confines seems an impossibility. Tell me, is Jacques a happy man?"

"No less happy than any other." I thought to myself that such a degree of happiness was not much. "I do know that he returns home each day stooped over and weary, as if his body has conformed to the task of bending over a desk all day. And he has told me, on more than one occasion, that he spends each workday watching the clock and waiting for the day to end."

"If this is what having a job means, and it is, do you — Victor D'Argent — wish to lead such a life?"

"I should say not," I answered, with a decisiveness that shocked me. "But what else can I do?"

"You must seek a position that is as appealing as possible, keeping in mind the qualities of the company and its leaders that I have surveyed for you. If you are able to acquire some position within such an organization, you must immediately begin preparing yourself to leave it."

"What?!" This was too incredible.

"Listen carefully, Victor D'Argent. Men fall into two categories: those who want a secure job, and those who want to be their own bosses. If you want to be one of the latter, you must begin to behave like a leader from the beginning. To the qualities of leadership I have already surveyed, I will add three more: courage, humility, and curiosity. How does one in a new job put these qualities into practice? Just so: Learn your new job well, so well that one day you will be able to march into the chief executive's office and volunteer to train your replacement!

"Once again, you look amazed," he continued, smiling at me, "but think a moment. The best way to prove that you are ready for a promotion is to demonstrate complete mastery of your duties, and complete mastery can only be demonstrated by teaching another. By offering to teach your job to another, you are declaring that you have grown beyond its demands.[†] Of course, this is something of a risk, and requires a measure of courage, because certain employers may understand your proposal as a resignation. But it is an entirely necessary risk, if you are ever to advance at all, and if you have developed a keen knowledge of your employer (as you must), it is — we may say — a *calculated* risk, and the courage it requires is not by any means foolhardy.

"Humility requires that you take full responsibility for both your mistakes and shortcomings. When something goes wrong, you must never blame subordinates, whether you are a clerk or a manager or an owner. Doing so implies that you are beyond error and beyond reproach, and such an image of oneself is not only foolish, it will lead to destructive relations with others, and eventually to the failure of any enterprise. For any task that you oversee, whether small or large, you must be thoroughly familiar with every step and every

---

[†] EDITOR'S NOTE: The "train your replacement" concept was developed further in the United States by industrialist Clement Watt, who detailed the process in a famous 1919 essay, *Something You Should Know.*

aspect, and hold yourself accountable for every facet of the operation. Praise others when things go right; blame yourself when they do not. Only if you practice this at every point in your career will you learn to be a leader.

"Both courage and humility are intimately tied to curiosity. For to be knowledgeable enough to direct others in any task, one must understand their duties completely. Your friend Jacques will never be a leader, because he disdains familiarity with the other workers in the mill, and knows nothing of their work experiences. He does not realize that the papers that cross his desk refer to and depend upon the day to day labor of a number of others. He would rather stay enclosed in his small world, within his small cell of an office, maintaining his small mind."

At that moment, I recognized that this description of Jacques was remarkably accurate, but that I had not acknowledged the smallness of the man until now.

"Curiosity," the Count continued, "will lead you to watch the work of others, to ask questions of them, to help them at times when you are not otherwise occupied. Doing so, you expand the circumference of your intelligence and your abilities. Doing so, you can become a great man."

I thrilled at this idea, for truly, I had never thought of myself as capable of any sort of greatness.

"I see that we have granted both of your 'wishes', have we not?"

"How is this so?" I asked, a bit puzzled.

The Count laughed. "This morning you asked for the wealth that is your birthright, gold. I explained that acquiring gold is an easy matter, and have given you all the basic knowledge that you will need to do so, once you have earned the capital to begin. However, the wealth that is *your* birthright is the birthright of every person, and it is a personal and a spiritual matter rather than a matter of finances. The qualities I have associated with leadership in business are those same qualities that will bring you personal and spiritual wealth. For financial success, you will find, is a by-product of *uncommon behavior*, which entails the virtues of leadership that include — as I have said — the courage to face the unknown and risk failure or misunderstanding, the humility to praise others and blame yourself (rather than the

opposite), and the curiosity to broaden your mind
and experience. While financial success will follow
from these virtues, it will become less important
for you than the recognition that your soul has
taken flight, that you have reached a higher plane
of consciousness. From this new vantage point,
you will see that the common world of common
thoughts is most absurd, and that almost all of
those who crave gold really need to ascend beyond
their common selves, but will never wake up to
this possibility."

"And will I, as you put it, 'wake up'?"

"You began to wake up when you took the uncommon road out of the Rue de Sagesse. You des-
ignated yourself as one of the chosen, one of those
whose soul yearns to prosper."

"But my mind kept telling me merely to seek
gold," I insisted.

"Yes, your mind will often cloud your true
needs. Here, I have tried to reveal them to you.
But you can only pursue the truth if you become
alert to those thoughts that merely reproduce
common ideas and wishes. Do not let them guide
you. Instead, listen to my voice — for it is also
your own. Let it become an insistent whisper

within you, deep in your being, beyond your thoughts.

"Do you know why my castle is surrounded by mustard trees?" he asked suddenly.

"Are you, perhaps, creating some allusion to the passage in Matthew that compares the kingdom of heaven to a mustard plant?"

"Yes, you have discovered this," he laughed. "But there is more about the mustard seed in the book of Matthew, and also in the book of Luke. Listen."

He arose and walked to his books, pulling a large, red and gold volume from the top shelf. Seated again, he read to me:

> *Now the parable is this: The [mustard] seed is the word of God . . . .*
> *And that which fell among thorns are they, which, when they have heard, go forth, and are choked with cares and riches and pleasures of this life, and bring no fruit to perfection . . . . Take heed therefore how ye hear: for whosoever hath, to him shall be given; and whosoever hath not, from him*

shall be taken even that which he
seemeth to have.

The Count looked up at me, and spoke with great seriousness. "The planting of seeds is a great gift. You have been chosen to receive it. If you go forth into the world of books, according to your interest, remember what I have spoken to you. Share my words with those who, like yourself, find themselves at a crossroads in life, filled with inspiration and uncertainty. And before you leave this world, see that a few printed copies of this wisdom see the light of day. Be assured that whoever seeks, finds, and reads these words of mine is also one of the chosen, and they may also bear fruit if they hear truly."

He paused, and arose, grasping my hand warmly and speaking with a tone of finality: "I have spoken, you have heard, now we must part."

The sun was descending as we walked toward the castle gate. I expected to meet once again the impossibly narrow door that had faced me that morning. But now the opening was perfectly easy to pass, and I was confounded. Walking through, I turned back to the Count and asked one final question.

"What became of the narrow door?"

"Your mind created it," he said. "Now you know better." Then he laughed.

I waved good-bye, and turned toward the sun on the horizon. As I traversed the path away from the castle, the sun seemed to stand still, so that I could not tell whether it was setting, or rising.

❧

Colophon

This book is typeset in 11 pt Bauer Bodoni Book and is printed on 100 gram Munken B.O.F. matt cream bookwove paper. It is section sewn with separate ends, bound inside 3mm cover boards with square back, and covered in Balacron dark green leatherette, with gold stamping on the front cover.